CITY UNIVERSITY LONDON

Afasic *unlocking speech and language*

With thanks for your contribution to
***Lost for Words, Lost for Life* confere**
June 15-17th 2011

THE SLI HANDBOOK

What **YOU** need to know about
Specific Language Impairment:

What it means, looks, feels and
sounds like, and how to get help

Credits

Compiled and written by I CAN and Afasic
Author: Mandy Grist with input from Lisa Knowles,
Linda Lascelles, Alison Huneke
Produced by Kendall Beaudry
Illustrated by Marc Ellerby
Designed by Deborah Ripley

Commissioned by The Communication Trust
Funded by the *Hello* campaign and supported by
the Communication Champion

I CAN
8 Wakley Street
London
EC1V 7QE
ican.org.uk

0207 843 2552

Registered Charity Number 210031

Afasic
1st Floor
20 Bowling Green Lane
London EC1R 0BD
afasic.org.uk

0207 490 9410

Registered Charity Number 1045617

Contents

Introduction

This book is for parents of children with specific language impairment (SLI). It outlines what children and young people struggle with and describes the type of support that children and young people with SLI need. It also illustrates how SLI is different to other speech, language and communication needs.

The book will help guide parents through what is a complex difficulty, outlining how to get a diagnosis and secure the right support for their child at nursery or school. It also signposts organisations who can offer help and support.

Although primarily written with parents in mind, this book will also be useful for teachers and early years staff to better identify and support children and young people in their care who have SLI.

What is SLI?

Children with Specific Language Impairment, or SLI, are as able and healthy as other children in all ways, with one exception; they have enormous difficulty talking and sometimes also understanding language.

SLI is a term that is used to describe difficulties with learning and using language. These difficulties are not associated with factors such as general learning difficulties, or other conditions, such as cerebral palsy, hearing impairment or autistic spectrum disorders. Children with SLI are often as clever as any other child of their age but they still have difficulties with speech and language, hence the term 'specific', as difficulties are specific to this area.

A child with SLI will not develop speech and language skills in the expected way. More often than not, there is no obvious reason for this difficulty.

This means, for example, a child with SLI might be bright, but struggle to understand the language used in the classroom. They may have lots of ideas but find it hard to make sentences to say what they are thinking, but they do not have any other condition that may be causing these problems.

SLI looks different in all children, and is really complicated to understand because we don't know the cause. We know that the speech and language part of the brain does not develop in the same way as others, even though there are no other problems, and that genes play an important part in causing SLI. Unfortunately there is no medical test to see if a child has SLI or not.

Studies have shown that in 5 year olds, SLI affects about 2 children in every classroom (about 7%) and that it is more common in boys than girls.

What can go wrong?

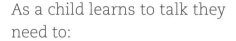

As a child learns to talk they need to:

- Learn to **understand words, sentences and conversations** (often referred to as receptive language)

- Learn how to **talk using words and sentences** (often referred to as expressive language)

- Know how to **use language the right way socially** with others. For example, listening as well as talking, taking turns and talking to a teacher differently than to a friend (often called pragmatic language)

- **Say speech sounds correctly** so that they can be understood by others

A child with SLI does not develop the ability to do these things in the right way. They may have difficulty in all of these areas, or in one more than the others.

Specialists might talk about a child having a 'spiky profile' which means they might be good at some aspects of language, but not others. For example, they may have good understanding but poor vocabulary and expressive language.

Children with SLI can have a range of difficulties

I struggle with reading and writing.

I can't always say what I want to even though I've got the ideas.

I can talk in sentences but my speech can be difficult to understand.

I can sound muddled and disorganised so my talking is difficult to follow.

In most ways, I'm as able as friends in my class.

I can find it hard to join in and work or play with others.

I don't understand what lots of words mean.

I might have behavioural problems and get frustrated or withdrawn.

I am quite smart, so even though I don't understand the words, I watch so I know what's going on.

Sometimes I know the word I want but I just can't remember it when I need it.

I can't follow when people say long sentences - it's confusing.

What else do we know about SLI?

All children with SLI are different.

SLI can be identified when children are at preschool (or even earlier), at primary school and possibly not until they are at secondary school.

Their difficulties can be 'hidden' for a long time, because:

• They can look like something else, for example, poor reading, or poor behaviour

• Lots of people don't recognise SLI or understand it, because it is complicated

• Children can be bright and able in many ways, despite having SLI

• Children sometimes become good at hiding their difficulties

Children with SLI usually have difficulty learning at school, despite the fact that their thinking skills and academic potential are often on a level with other children of their age.

Children with SLI won't just 'pick it up.' They can't learn language in the same way as other children, just by being spoken to and encouraged. They need language to be taught – often in a specific way. They need to get the right support to do this so that they can learn and develop to their full potential. Without this support, SLI may cause a child lifelong difficulties.

Some children with SLI have very severe and complex needs. These children will make progress and can be taught a whole range of strategies that will help them manage their communication. However, due to the severity of their SLI, these children will always have some difficulty with communication.

Children with SLI will probably find social activities difficult too, for example after school clubs and youth groups. They will need a really supportive environment with people who understand their difficulties to help them in these situations.

Some children with SLI have relatively moderate needs. With the right support they have the potential to make excellent progress.

The type of difficulties a child with SLI has can change as they get older. For example, they may get better at understanding what other people are saying but still struggle to put sentences together.

It is really important that a regular assessment is carried out to make sure that a child with SLI is getting the right support at the right time. The help that they need might change as they get older.

The terminology used to describe SLI can be very confusing. People often use different words to describe the difficulties that a child with SLI might be having. Specialists might use different words to describe different aspects of SLI. Some of the different terms for describing SLI can be found in the Appendix (page 106).

ASD

SLI

SEN

SLT

AAC

Comprehension

Expressive language disorder

Specific Language Impairment

SLC

Pragmatic language impairment

SLCN

Receptive language difficulties

Speech sound disorders

SLI or general learning difficulties?

Children with SLI do not have a general learning difficulty. This means that they are able to use the skills and abilities they have, like being quick to learn things visually, to help their learning.

Andre has SLI and does not understand a lot of instructions the teacher gives. When the teacher asks the red group to get out the equipment for PE, Andre knows the teacher has given an instruction because he is carefully watching him. He sees his friends in the red group move towards the equipment cupboard and runs so he is one of the first to get things out for the lesson. He knows what equipment is needed and where it needs to go in the hall because he remembers what happened in PE last week. No one would guess he didn't understand what his teacher said. Andre is good at using strategies to help him cope.

Billy has general learning difficulties. He doesn't realise that the teacher has given an instruction and doesn't understand that he is part of a group called 'red group', and that the instruction applies to him. Billy doesn't remember last week's PE lesson so he doesn't know what equipment is needed. Because of his general learning difficulties, Billy needs a simple individual instruction to be able to join in with his class mates.

SLI and Speech, Language and Communication Needs (SLCN)

Children with speech and language difficulties are often described as having speech, language and communication needs (SLCN). This is a general term used to describe any kind of difficulties with speech and language. Children might have SLCN for a whole range of reasons, e.g. associated with a learning difficulty or physical difficulty or because their language is delayed.

ASD   SLI
Language delay   Stammer
Cerebral palsy   Down syndrome
Learning difficulties

SLI fits under this umbrella term, but these children have very specific difficulties with language. They don't have any underlying syndrome, e.g. Down syndrome; or physical needs, e.g. cleft palate; sensory impairments, e.g. hearing impairment; or general learning difficulties. Sometimes children with other conditions such as dyslexia or autistic spectrum disorder, will have language difficulties. These language difficulties may look similar to the difficulties a child with SLI has but they are actually very different.

When children are very young it can be difficult to be sure which type of problem they have.

The most important thing to remember is that children with SLI have very specific language difficulties which are not caused by another condition, like dyslexia – we don't know the cause.

SLI or language delay?

Some children have a 'language delay'. This means that their language develops in the normal way, but at a slower rate than other children. They often sound young for their age.

Children with SLI are not simply slow to learn language. They do not have a 'language delay'. Sometimes SLI and language delay can look similar, but a child with language delay is more likely to 'catch up'. A child with SLI will not, and will need specialist help from a speech and language therapist and/ or a specialist teacher.

Rex is 5 and has delayed language. He has an immature vocabulary and puts together simple sentences, often missing out small words like 'it', 'and', 'to', 'at'. He understands a little bit more than he can say and sounds like a younger child, more like a 3½ year old.

Omar is 6 and has SLI. He understands everything that is said to him, though he struggles to put words into sentences. Sometimes he can't find the word he needs or puts words in the wrong order in sentences. Omar sometimes sounds a bit like Rex, but his speech is more difficult to understand.

REX

OMAR

SLI in preschool children

Early signs of SLI

Young children with SLI are able and bright in many ways but they will take longer to start to talk than other children and may only use single words. You might notice that they don't respond to language as others do. Parents often worry that their child cannot hear what is being said to them.

Preschool children with SLI can do lots of things

• They are as able as other children of their age when they don't have to use and understand language to do the task, for example, doing a jigsaw, or building with toys

• They can be good at socialising in familiar places and with familiar people

• They often understand the language used at home when it is based around family routines like getting dressed and mealtimes

• They like to play with other children, though can struggle when lots of language is needed, e.g. in roleplay games

• They often have good skills in tasks that don't involve language, for example, puzzles or physical activities

Preschool children with SLI will find some of the following things difficult:

Understanding language
• They make slow, little, or no response when someone speaks to them. You might need to repeat an instruction several times and make it much simpler

• They often rely on visual information to get things right, for example, watching others to find out what an instruction means

Using language
• They may not use many different words

• They find it hard to link words together to make sentences

• The language they use can often sound jumbled up and can be difficult to understand

• They may point or show what they want rather than say it

• How they say speech sounds can be very slow to develop and so speech is difficult to understand

Social and learning skills

• Although they often are bright and able, they find it difficult to learn. This is because lots of how we learn is through listening, understanding, talking and interacting with others, which they find hard

• They often find joining in with activities chosen by an adult difficult (and are often considered to have 'bad' behaviour or be disruptive)

• They can find new routines or interruptions to routines hard to deal with (for example, lunch happening at a different time than expected). They may rely on routines to understand what is happening, so can get upset when these change unexpectedly

• Although they might be sociable, they find it hard to make friends or play with other children. Joining in games is hard, so they might find it easier to play alone

• Imaginative and pretend games – where children need to talk lots – will be difficult. They may opt for physical play, construction, or sand and water games where less language is needed

Things you can do to help a preschool child

If you are concerned about a child's speech and language development you should contact your local speech and language therapy (SLT) service. You can find details of your local service on the Talking Point website: **talkingpoint.org.uk/talkinglinks.**

You might find it useful to try some of the following ideas to help a child that you are concerned about:

• It really helps if you say a child's name before you ask them to do something. That way they know you are talking to them

• Break down what you want them to do into small steps. Instead of saying, *'Tea's ready.. but before you come can you tidy up please?'* say, *'Toys away, tea time.'*

• Give a child lots of clues about what you want them to do, if they don't understand. You could use your hands to gesture, or even draw pictures to help them

• Encourage a child to communicate in any way, not just through words. Actions and gestures will help to develop words

• If a child says something in the wrong way, repeat the right way back to them instead of correcting them. For example, if a child says *'Dog him sit...'* Repeat back, *'Yes, the dog is sitting.'*

• When talking to a child allow plenty of gaps around the sentences that you are using to a child. This will allow them time to think about what you have said and maybe to formulate a response

James is 4 years old and has SLI. He is a bright boy who loves construction toys and games. When building models at nursery he finds it hard to understand what his teacher wants him to do when she tells the group. However, when he has the instruction book in front of him, with picture diagrams, James is able to build a beautiful model as well as any of the other children.

Ellie is 4 years old and has SLI. She is a bright little girl who enjoys joining in with all the activities that the group in the nursery do. When her teacher asks the children to put their cups in the sink after snack time, Ellie doesn't do it even though she knows the teacher has asked her to do something. When she sees what the others are doing she quickly joins in. Ellie watches the other children to help her understand what is happening and what she needs to do.

JAMES

ELLIE

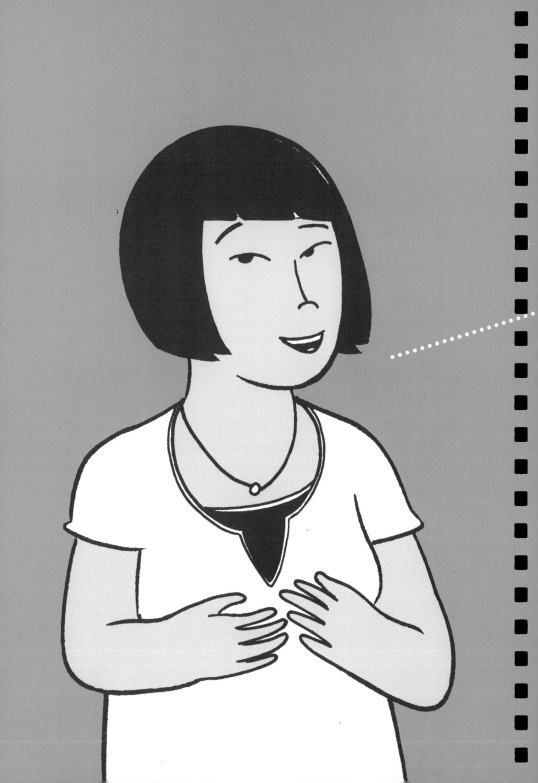

SLI in primary years

Primary-aged children with SLI can do lots of things

• They are usually as bright and able as their classmates when they don't have to rely on language to learn

• They can follow situations and routines that are familiar

• They are often good with practical tasks, for example, they can follow picture instructions to make a Lego model

• They tend to enjoy and succeed more in practical tasks at school, like science experiments (but they might get stuck if they need to understand the words)

• They understand things like facial expressions and body language and understand about feelings, even if they don't know the words for them

When children with SLI learn language, they don't follow the usual pattern that you would see in most children. They have what is often called atypical development; it means that their language doesn't sound like a child of their age and often sounds strange or unusual.

Primary-aged children with SLI will find some of the following things difficult:

Understanding language

• They find it hard to learn and understand the meanings of words

• They find it hard to understand language about things in the past or future

• Words and sentences that can mean more than one thing are difficult e.g. *'Pull your socks up.'*

• They might respond to just part of an instruction, usually the beginning or end

Using language

• They use short sentences, often with words missed out or in the wrong order so they sound muddled or unusual, e.g. *'Man is dog him chase.'*

• Using the right words can be difficult so they might use a word that means something similar, e.g. calling an 'island' a 'beach'; make up words e.g. 'cuttergrasser' to describe a lawnmower; or talk around words; *'It's that thingy that the doctors use to listen to your heart.'*

• They find it hard to make up stories. This shows in their written work as well as when they are talking, with stories being muddled or in the wrong order, making them difficult to follow

• Speech may be unclear as they have not developed their sounds in the right way

Social skills
• They often have difficulty understanding the rules of a game and so find it hard to join in

• They can find it hard to join in group conversations, because there is too much language

• Using language to organise play and activities with friends is hard

Things you could do to help a child with SLI during their primary years

The following things are useful for helping a child with SLI. Remember, you should contact your local speech and language therapist if you are concerned about a child's speech and language development. You can find details of your local service on the Talking Point website: **talkingpoint.org.uk/talkinglinks**

• Always say their name before you ask them to do something or give an instruction. This helps them to know that you are talking to them which means that they can listen better

• Tell them which bits of information to focus on, e.g. listen for who is in the story

• Make understanding easier by giving shorter instructions, and leaving a bit of time for them to process what you've said and give a response

• Check that they have understood. You could ask them to tell you if there are any words that they did not know, and ask a couple of questions, *'Where are you going to put it?'* to make sure that they know what you have asked them to do

• Help them link new words and ideas to what they know already – e.g. *'Enormous, that means very big. Remember the elephant we saw in the zoo? He was enormous.'*

• Give them good models to copy rather than correct what they have said by repeating back what they said the right way. It can also be helpful to add another word or two to their sentence to help them develop their talking, for example, if they said, *'That man walking.'* You could say, *'Yes, that man is walking on the grass.'*

• Help them learn skills so they can join in with other children, for example, taking turns in games and listening to what others have said. You can do this by playing any games that you might have at home

Duncan has SLI. He is very clever in many ways but finds it hard to understand the language that is used at school. In maths the teacher gives him a problem, *'Three buses were in the depot, five were on the road and two were at the bus stop. How many buses altogether?'* Duncan cannot answer, he just looks blankly at her. The sum got lost in the words. When she writes down the sum 3+5+2 he has no trouble working out the answer because he does not need to use language.

Eve is 7 years old. She has been asked to write a story based on some work that the class has already done. She has lots of ideas and is keen to show the teacher all that she has understood. Eve finds it hard to plan for her story and her ideas get in a muddle. Her sentences don't make sense and her story ends up being confusing and hard to follow. Eve is as clever as the other children in her class, but she has SLI and struggles with expressive language.

DUNCAN

EVE

SLI in secondary years

Secondary-aged children with SLI can do lots of things well

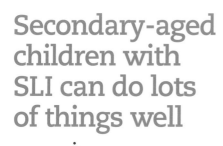

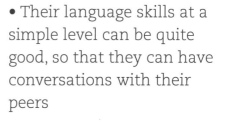

• They are as able as their classmates, when they don't need to use language. However by this age their SLI will have had a big impact on the way they learn and will often be affecting their school performance

• Their language skills at a simple level can be quite good, so that they can have conversations with their peers

• They can become good at hiding their difficulties

• They pick up on routines and find ways to manage their difficulties

• They are often good at and prefer practical tasks at school, for example, experiments in science, even though they find the language for these difficult

• They like to have friends and try to socialise with others

Secondary-aged children find certain things difficult:

Understanding language

• They may be slow to answer when spoken to, or need to ask for information to be repeated

• They have difficulties learning and understanding more complicated vocabulary that they come across in the classroom which then impacts on their comprehension of the lesson

• They struggle to understand sarcasm and some of the language of adolescence that have different meanings from those expected, or are made up – e.g. wicked, tight, chillax

• They find it hard to understand non-literal language such as idioms, metaphors and multiple meanings; where one word can mean more than one thing

Using language

• They find it hard to use 'good' sentences, even though they know how, and find more complicated language such as idioms, metaphors and multiple meanings hard to use

• Their stories or longer pieces of speech or writing don't have enough detail or are hard to follow

Learning and social skills

• They have difficulty working independently and prioritising. This might mean that despite being able to do the work, they struggle to complete it on time

• They find school social life hard because they may have difficulties keeping up with conversations, recognising social 'rules' and understanding that other people have a different point of view

• Their emotional problems may mean that they get frustrated or behave in a way that can seem naughty or challenging. This might be verbal or physical outbursts or showing little or no response which might make them seem passive

• They often have poor organisation skills

• Their language difficulties have considerable impact on skills needed for work experience, interviews and ultimately in the workplace

Things you could do to help a secondary-aged child with SLI

The following ideas will help a child with SLI. You should contact your local speech and language therapy service if you are concerned about a child's communication skills. You can find details of your local service on the Talking Point website:

talkingpoint.org.uk/talkinglinks

• Make sure that you give them time to think about what you have said. They will need longer than most people to process information, so try and leave a few seconds for them to reply

• Try to avoid tricky parts of language, such as idioms, 'I'm all ears' or metaphors, like 'Life is a journey' because they make language even more confusing for them

• Encourage them to tell you when they have not understood what you have said and help them to work out which bits were difficult

• Be honest. If you haven't understood what they have said, say so and try to work it out between you

• Talk through strategies that will help them to organise themselves, and help them to practise using these

• Acknowledge and recognise their skills and support them to use these to help communication

• Work out strategies that help them with communication, e.g. 'rehearsing' what people have said so they can remember and practise in their head

Yusuf is 13 years old. His SLI means he finds it hard to listen to instructions and understand the language used at school. Yusuf really enjoys PE and is good at sport. During PE lessons however he finds it hard to follow the instructions that his teacher is giving out. He doesn't always understand all of the rules of the games they play. Yusuf watches what the others in his class are doing, meaning that he does all of the exercises that the PE teacher gives them, but is always one step behind the others.

Harry is 15 years old and is very bright in many ways. He is frequently in trouble because he does not often hand his homework in on time, even though he is a keen pupil. Harry struggles to organise himself and finds it hard to remember which piece of homework needs to be in on which day. He needs to use his homework diary to remind him, but is not usually organised enough to write down what he needs to do and when. Even when he remembers to write his homework down, the information comes too quickly and he doesn't get it all down in time.

YUSUF

HARRY

Does my child have SLI?

How can I find out if my child has SLI?

This diagram and the following pages show a typical journey that a family might go on as they are finding out about their child's SLI. This journey is often a cycle, time-consuming and sometimes frustrating, and the processes and waiting times are different depending on where you live.

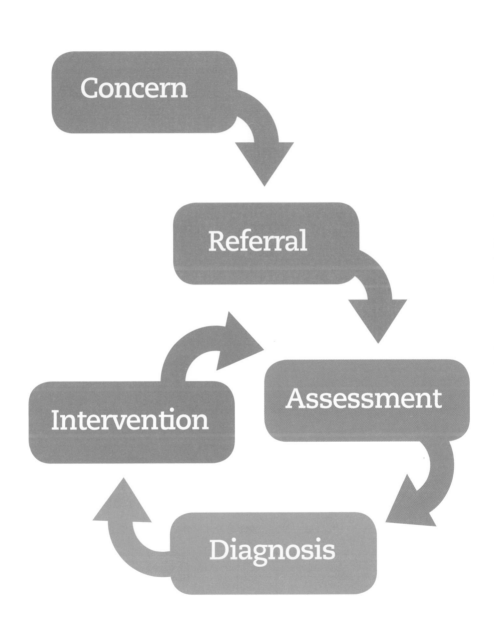

Concern

You or someone else that knows your child may have concerns about the way they are learning to talk or understand...

Referral

If you are concerned about your child's speech and language skills, you need to take them to see a speech and language therapist (SLT). You can refer directly to your local speech and language therapy service and you can find details of your local service on the Talking Point website: **talkingpoint.org.uk/talkinglinks**.

Often your child's health visitor, teacher or GP will make a referral after talking to you about any concerns that they might have, though you can refer yourself if they don't feel there is an issue and you are still concerned. You will be placed on a waiting list to see an SLT and the waiting list times are different according to where you live.

Assessment

To find out if your child does have SLI, or any other needs, an assessment will need to be carried out, initially by a speech and language therapist (SLT). This might involve your child looking at picture books, playing with toys and talking to the therapist, dependent on their child's age. The therapist will also talk to you about your concerns.

Other professionals will probably see your child too. This might be done in a clinic or hospital, or possibly at your child's school.

A re-assessment will also be done to review how your child is developing and how their needs are changing, following any intervention that they might have.

Diagnosis

From the assessment, the therapist will work out where your child might be struggling. Your child will usually be given a diagnosis of SLI if they are assessed and found to be as able as other children of their age but have the types of difficulties with speech and language that have been described earlier. This type of assessment and possible diagnosis might happen over quite a long time. Your child might be seen several times by several people including an SLT, teacher, educational psychologist and often a children's doctor. This varies enormously dependent on where you live.

Intervention

The people working with your child will decide, in discussion with you, about the best ways to support your child. For a child with SLI this might mean that they have individual, group or school based speech and language therapy, and possibly support from other people like a specialist teacher. This will depend on their age, the types of difficulties that they have and where they go to school. Therapists will work closely with schools and parents to support children, through training and joint working as well as direct therapy. You may be given ideas on where you can find out further information, for example, organisations such as Afasic, I CAN, Parent Partnership. The length of time that your child will be supported depends on the type of needs they have, how severe they are, and what services are available locally.

Who can help
my child?

These are some of the professionals who can help

Health professionals

Speech and Language Therapists assess, diagnose and treat children and young people with speech, language and communication needs and provide advice to others, e.g. teachers.

A **Paediatrician** is a doctor who treats children. Some paediatricians specialise in children with developmental disorders.

Occupational Therapists can help children with a range of developmental difficulties affecting their co-ordination, balance, motor skills, sensory integration and organisation.

An **Audiologist** is a healthcare scientist who assesses, diagnoses and rehabilitates patients with hearing problems.

SPEECH AND LANGUAGE THERAPIST

PAEDIATRICIAN

OCCUPATIONAL THERAPIST

AUDIOLOGIST

EDUCATIONAL PSYCHOLOGIST

SENCO

TEACHING ASSISTANT

EARLY YEARS ADVISORY TEACHER

Education professionals

Educational Psychologists assess children's skills for learning and the way that they learn.

The **Special Educational Needs Co-ordinator (SENCO)** is the person who is responsible for co-ordinating all the information about special educational needs (SEN) in a school.

A **Teaching Assistant** works in a classroom with the teacher. Often they help the children who have SEN by giving them extra support.

An **Early Years Advisory Teacher** helps nurseries and other early years settings identify and support children with various forms of SEN, including SLI.

A **Specialist Teacher** has additional expertise in SLI and advises teachers in mainstream schools. Sometimes they work directly with the children.

SPECIALIST TEACHER

Finding private practitioners

Sometimes parents do not want to wait to see a professional to find out about their child, or they would like another opinion.

You can consult many professionals privately, including speech and language therapists and educational psychologists. There is a charge for these services, however it is possible that this may be covered under private medical insurance, although this is not usually the case. Terms do vary, though, so parents are advised to check their policies carefully.

You can find a private speech and language therapist by going to the website run by ASLTIP (The Association of Speech and Language Therapists in Independent Practice) at **helpwithtalking.com**. From there you can search for a therapist by geographical location, the age range of your child, and type of expertise you would like.

You can get information about how to find a private educational psychologist from the website of the British Psychological Society: **bps.org.uk**.

To find a private occupational therapist, go to the website run by Occupational Therapists in Independent Practice: **otip.co.uk**.

To find a private physiotherapist, go to the website run by the Organisation of Chartered Physiotherapists in Private Practice: **physiofirst.org.uk**.

Some specialist schools for children with SLCN offer assessment services. For more information visit:

- **ican.org.uk/assessments**

- **moorhouseschool.co.uk**

- **witherslackgroup.co.uk/ belle-vue-assessment- centre**

Where will my child go to school?

Children with SLI can go to a range of different types of school, depending on the level of their need, the complexity of their language impairment and on what schools are available locally to them.

Different local authorities have different guidelines that they work to, and all children with SLI are different, so there are no rules about where a child will go to school; it varies according to where you live. Usually children will go to one of the following types of school, although most children are likely to go to their local mainstream school.

Mainstream Nursery, Primary and Secondary School

Most children with SLI attend a mainstream nursery or school. To help a child with SLI learn as best they can, the school will need to provide a communication-supportive environment. This will make sure that wherever possible, language is not a barrier to learning. Children with SLI are often supported by a teaching assistant, often working closely with an speech and language therapist and sometimes with a specialist teacher.

Specialist Speech and Language Schools

There are a small number of special schools that cater specifically for children with SLI. Generally speaking, they take children whose needs are particularly complex or severe, or who live in areas that do not have the right language provision. They are usually non-maintained or independent, i.e. not run by the local authority.

Language Resource Section (sometimes called a unit, base or centre)

This is a special class, for children with speech and language difficulties in a mainstream school. The unit has only a small group of children and is run by a specialist teacher, SLT and teaching assistant. Children spend some of their time in the unit (often for lessons like English and maths) and some of their time in the mainstream class. Staff in the resource base work closely with mainstream staff.

Local Authority Special Schools

Sometimes children with SLI will go to a local special school that caters for a whole range of different special educational needs. Children will be taught in small classes and an SLT will support them.

What does a communication-supportive environment look like?

In a primary school you should expect to see...

The teacher will say a child's name when asking a question or giving an instruction to make sure they are paying attention.

Susan, can you name a type of animal?

Classroom language is kept simple and repeated if necessary.

Any type of animal.

A reptile!

The classroom layout ensures children with SLI can be seated at the front facing the teacher.

Staff will point and gesture to support what they are saying.

Can anyone tell me what type of animal a tiger is?

TIGER

Children are given time to respond to questions and are allowed to plan before starting their work.

Susan, I am going to ask Billy first and then I am going to ask you.

SNAKE

The classroom should not be too cluttered and equipment should be clearly marked.

PENCILS

BLACK PENS

GLUESTICKS

SCISSORS

LINED PAPER

PLAIN PAPER

Children are given help and guidance about how to work in groups.

Maybe Mark can write about the mammals and Anna can work on birds.

Then both work on your collage.

Children are encouraged to work at their own level so they don't misunderstand or become stressed.

Ahmed, are you fine working on just the writing today and finishing the collage tomorrow?

Yes, Mr Cadwell.

In a secondary school you should expect to see...

The school is laid out well so pupils with SLI can easily find their way around the buildings. Colour coded rooms is one example.

MR THOMAS SCIENCE 8DTH E39

MONDAY
TUESDAY
WEDNESDAY

Pupils with SLI are seated at the front of the class. Information is left on the white board for adequate time to allow pupils to read and understand.

Morning all! Today we'll be looking at the properties of metal, so you'll need your books out.

Teachers do not talk for the entire lesson. Difficult words and instructions are explained.

You'll be working mostly from worksheets today but don't worry, we'll all work through a few examples together, first.

POP

Pupils are shown when they have done something incorrect or misunderstood an instruction. They are taught how to help themselves when this happens.

You've got a bit wrong there, Simon.

Oh, really?

Yes, let me show you again and then you can give it another try.

Pupils are encouraged to work together in groups and are supported if needed.

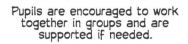

Do you see how Sandra's worked it out?

Yeah.

If Sandra doesn't mind, maybe ask her to give you a hand.

Helpful visual supports are used in all classes.

These illustrated sheets may help you, Simon.

Thanks.

Specific words relating to each subject and taught to SLI pupils before the lesson.

"Hypothesis" means what you think is going to happen.

Oh.

There is support for study skills such as note taking, revising, organising homework to help pupils with SLI organise themselves better.

Remember to take notes as you go along, Simon.

All schools need to make sure that they provide the best learning environment for children and young people with SLI, regardless of the type of school that they are. This means that they need to make sure they provide a communication-supportive environment.

They need to have the following features that would be considered to be good practice in providing support for children and young people with SLI:

• Lots of visual support systems to help with understanding. Things like timetables on the wall, targets shown on the whiteboard, picture cards and photos are really good

• A speech and language therapist who has spoken to the staff in the classroom, to explain SLI and what it means for a child in their school

• Teaching assistants that have received training from a speech and language therapist to support children with SLI

• Information is presented in a variety of ways. This means that teaching would include the use of real objects, practical activities, pictures and video

• Teachers who have received training on how to make the classroom environment – and their own instructions, questions and comments – communication-supportive

• Lesson planning that includes explicit opportunities to build speaking and listening skills for all children and which incorporates therapy goals for individual children

• Information that is shared about pupils with SLI between teachers and schools

• Information given to parents about the way the school supports special educational needs and how to contact people who support their child, like the Special Educational Needs Co-ordinator (SENCO)

On the following pages we will see how different types of schools are helping Jack, Ethan, Emma and Craig with their SLI

...regardless of the type of school that they are.

Mainstream schools, as well as language resources and specialist schools for pupils with SLI, are required to provide a communication-supportive environment.

In reality, some schools are able to do this really well, while others find it more difficult. (A list of helpful questions to ask a school when visiting is included in appendix 2).

Language resources and specialist schools however are likely to provide a good communication-supportive environment in a more in-depth way, and will have staff that are knowledgeable and skilled at working with pupils with SLI.

The following case studies give some examples of the types of support a child can get in different settings.

Mainstream primary school

Jack

Jack is 7 years old and in a mainstream school. His SLI means that he has difficulties understanding and using language, particularly affecting his ability to follow long instructions and make sentences to express what he means.

When Jack is in the classroom, he sits near to the front of the class, facing the teacher. The teacher gestures to help keep Jack focused and to give him extra clues about what he is learning. If she wants him to respond to a question or instruction, the teacher always says his name first so that he knows to listen.

Jack knows what the targets for learning are as they are clearly shown. on the whiteboard.

The teaching assistant (TA) in the classroom checks with Jack that he has understood the task before he begins, and if new vocabulary is introduced the TA will reinforce the learning by showing Jack with pictures or drawings if needed. It is also sometimes necessary for her to give Jack instructions again when he has not understood, using different words or simpler sentences. She is encouraging him to be more independent by telling the teacher when he doesn't understand.

Jack is given some time to plan his work, for example, during a literacy task when the children are asked to create a story. He uses a story planning sheet to help him make sure that he includes all the important parts (one of a range of resources that he uses to support his learning).

Staff on duty at playtime are aware that Jack and his friends sometimes need help to resolve difficulties. They have knowledge about the amount of information that Jack can understand and they help him to take part in the game by supporting him to join in in the right way by, for example, pointing out that he needs to wait before he can have his turn. The school operates a buddy system, and older children are encouraged to help the younger pupils like Jack during playtime if they see them having difficulties.

Mainstream Secondary School

Ethan

Ethan is 13 and attends mainstream secondary school. He has difficulties understanding long or complicated sentences and learning new vocabulary. He doesn't usually know when he doesn't understand and can become frustrated and angry when he feels he is struggling.

In the classroom Ethan sits near to the teacher, and the teacher always makes sure that they stop speaking when they are facing away to write on the whiteboard. All of Ethan's teachers know the things to do that that are helpful to him when they are teaching, and can refer to his 'communication passport' if they need reminding. This is a way of recording important information about a pupil, their particular strengths and

communication needs and ways of supporting these). All staff are aware that Ethan might find it difficult to understand some of the language that they might use e.g. idioms. Because of this, staff have asked the whole class to act as 'spotters' and let them know when they have used words that shouldn't be taken literally or are jokes, like 'Pull your socks up'. The 'spotters' then have to explain what the real meaning is.

The teaching staff think carefully about how difficult the lesson is for Ethan, and when appropriate keep a distance to allow him to work independently if possible. Sometimes staff need to check with Ethan that he has understood. They ask 'Do you know what to do?' and then follow up with 'Tell me'. The school have helped Ethan to be more independent by encouraging him to use and keep to-do lists.

At break times the supervising staff are aware of the difficulties that Ethan has, and ways to support him have been shared with all. Ethan has ongoing support from staff to help him manage his frustration and behavioural difficulties. For example, if he is getting too frustrated, or in danger of losing his temper, Ethan can take time out in the learning support room or the library.

Speech and language resource

Emma

Emma was referred for speech and language therapy when she was 3 years old. By the time she was 5 years old, she used very little language of her own, she often didn't reply if spoken to, and when she did speak she mostly used whole phrases that she had learned. She had difficulties understanding the meanings of words and sentences, and struggled to use her language in the right way socially. This affected her ability to learn and interact with children and adults.

When she started school she was placed in a language unit where she was taught by specialist staff. Whilst there, the speech and language therapist and specialist teaching staff worked together to support

When Emma was younger she went to school in a language unit where staff and therapists developed her language and social skills.

But because she was as bright as her fellow students, she was also taught in a mainstream class.

Skip on a few years and with a bit of support and hard work, she passed all her GCSE's and eventually her A-Levels. Well done, Emma!

Now she's applying all that hard work to a University degree in History.

and develop her language and social interaction skills. She spent some time in the mainstream part of school, where she was able to learn and benefit from their communication-supportive environment.

After two years, she had improved to the point that she was able to spend increasing amounts of time in a mainstream class. When she moved to secondary school she was able to go to a mainstream school with minimal support.

She passed all her GCSEs, went on to do A-levels and is now at university.

Specialist speech and language school

Craig

Craig's parents noticed that his speech and language were not developing in the same way that his brother's had and raised their concerns with his health visitor. Craig was assessed by a speech and language therapist and individual speech and language therapy at nursery.

Initial assessment: A multi-disciplinary assessment was eventually carried out and it was agreed that Craig had a severe specific speech and language impairment. In preparation for starting

school Craig was given a statement and he was provided with 13 hours of 1:1 teaching assistant support in school and intermittent blocks of speech and language therapy.

Little was done to provide training to Craig's teachers however, or to advise them on how to adapt their teaching to meet his needs. He received only intermittent blocks of speech and language therapy. He attended a mainstream school until the end of Year 2.

During Year 2 school staff felt he was unable to cope with the curriculum and understand the language level in a mixed Year 1/2 class, even with this level of support.

The Headteacher reported that he was becoming socially isolated and was unable to work on any task independently. His parents were also worried.

Re-assessment: Following on from these concerns the local authority requested a multi-disciplinary assessment at a special school where severe and complex speech, language and communication needs are the primary disability.

Change of support: Placement was offered and Craig joined the special school at the beginning of Year 3. He is currently in a class of 10 pupils with similar needs, in a visually supported environment with a reduced language level.

The curriculum is differentiated and delivered at a level appropriate for his needs. He receives intensive speech and language therapy individually, in small groups as well as class based input.

In addition there is close liaison between the class teacher and SLT, who plan targets jointly to ensure the language level is right for Craig.

Changing schools

Changing schools might be challenging

Children and young people with SLI and their families might find moving or changing school challenging. It might be a move from nursery to school, or primary to secondary school. It might be when starting new activities or clubs outside of school. There are some things that will help with these transitions:

• Information sharing is absolutely essential. This will include passing of information about a child's difficulties to a new teacher, or to new members of staff, including those who do not work in a classroom

• Reports and information from SLTs and other professionals should be shared and discussed, including information on ideas for support and changes to classroom work

• Detailed information about support strategies and resources should be passed to all involved with a child with SLI

• Assessment of needs should be ongoing. The nature and extent of a child's difficulties can change and therefore it is really important that a regular review and assessment is carried out. This will include A classroom assessment done by the teacher as well as an assessment from external professionals

• Parents should be involved in transitions as much as possible, so that they can support their child at home

• It might be helpful to visit a new school before the first day, to help a child get used to the changes

• Give a child as much information as you can about their new school, for example get some photos of the teachers they will work with. Older children might find it helpful to have a map of their new school that they can look at to prepare them

Planning for transition should begin as soon as possible in order to ease the process and may be written into objectives as part of the annual review process for children with a statement of SEN.

For more information about school transitions read, **Transition to Secondary School: Supporting Pupils with Speech, Language and Communication Needs** by Anne Ayre & Sue Roulstone, published by The Communication Trust at: **thecommunicationtrust.org.uk**

Also, Afasic has just published an information pack called, Transfer to Secondary School. To order online please visit: **afasicengland.org.uk/ publications/general- resources/**

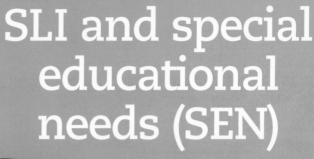

SLI and special educational needs (SEN)

Many children with SLI would be considered to have a special educational need (SEN). There are several steps that they may go through, although not all children with SLI will reach every stage.

Depending on how severe their SLI is, where they go to school, and how services are organised locally, this means that they may receive extra help at school and be part of the SEN system.

Early Years/ School Action

If your child is struggling, the nursery or school will do all they can to help them by giving them extra help and targets that are different to the rest of the class to help them make good progress – this level of support is called Early Years or School Action. Some children with SLI will be at this level in school and nursery.

Early Years/ School Action Plus

At this level the nursery or school will involve extra help from outside the school. For example, an SLT, to help them to try to make sure your child can make good progress. This might mean that children with SLI have special programmes of work to practise and/ or have special targets in the classroom that have been set by that professional. Lots of children with SLI will be at this level in school or nursery.

The SEN Code of Practice is the statutory guidance issued by the government to schools and local authorities about how they should support children with SEN, and it gives more detail about the SEN system.

Parents can download their own copy from: **direct.gov.uk/en/parents**

Formal assessment

In a very small number of cases the Local Authority will need to make a formal assessment of special educational needs and then consider whether or not to issue a statement for a child. This means they will ask the school, parents and other professionals, e.g. an SLT, to write a report about a child, and sometimes this will involve a formal assessment being carried out. From this information they decide if a child needs a statement. Parents may request a formal assessment is carried out but this does not mean that the authority must do it.

Statement

A statement is a legal document which describes a child's needs, the support that a child should get, and the school they will attend. The statement gives schools guidance and support to help a child with SLI, and describes any extra help that they might need, for example how much speech and language therapy they might get. If a school is sure that your child can't make good progress without this extra support they might put them forward for a statement. Quite a lot of children with SLI will have a statement.

If your child is identified as having SEN the Code of Practice states that schools and nurseries should draw up an Individual Education Plan (IEP) that gives detail about any support they receive that is additional to or different from the curriculum offered to all children.

Parents should be involved in drawing up the IEP as well as the child, if appropriate, and in monitoring their child's progress. If outside professionals, such as a speech and language therapist, are involved in supporting your child, they should also contribute to the IEP.

Many of the features listed in a communication-supportive environment in the previous chapter are the type of 'reasonable adjustments' that schools are legally required to make under Disability Discrimination legislation. Others might be part of the programme of support your child should have to help develop their speech and language skills, as set out in special educational law.

Making sure that your child's school meets their needs appropriately is likely to require ongoing collaboration and negotiation. You will find this easier to achieve if you have a good understanding of your child's needs and your legal entitlements.

If you are not happy with the support your child is getting, it is really important that you talk to the professionals supporting them. You can get advice about what to do from several of the organisations listed in the Useful Organisations section in the Appendix.

Further information on this can be found from your Parent-Partnership Service or the Afasic helpline 0845 355 5577 or the I CAN enquiry service 0845 225 4073.

Appendix 1

Acronym city: Breaking down the terminology

Term	Definition	For example
Articulation	Movement of the lips, tongue, teeth, and palate into specific patterns for speech.	
Atypical	Not following a normal or expected pattern (see also Disorder).	
Augmentative and Alternative Communication	Any method that can be used to support spoken communication. Often known as AAC.	Signing, symbols, high-tech communication aids
Communication-supportive environment	An environment that promotes the development of speech, language and communication skills, and that offers support to those that struggle with these things.	Inclusion of visual supports, careful monitoring of language levels
Comprehension	Understanding of spoken and written language.	
Disorder	Child is functioning below their age, but not following normal patterns of development.	

Term	Definition	For example
	Specific learning difficulties relating to literacy skills e.g. reading, spelling.	
Expressive language	Language a child uses for communication.	
Figurative language	Language that cannot be interpreted literally, even though you can understand all the words.	Idioms – 'Raining cats and dogs', Similes – 'Fight like a lion', Metaphors – 'Life's a journey.'
Grammar	The rules that dictate the way that words can be combined into sentences and longer strings of language, and the parts of language we can use to change meaning, for example plurals such as 'cats'. Grammar also allows us to know the order words must go in sentences, so that they make sense.	
Idioms	Short phrases used in a particular way, that cannot be interpreted and understood literally.	'Hit the roof.' 'Your room is like a pigsty.'

Term	Definition	For example
Jargon	Used by SLTs to refer to strings of sounds that have no meaning, but that 'sound' like adult speech as they have appropriate intonation patterns.	
Lexicon	The internal list of words a child knows (see also Vocabulary).	
Morphology	The rules that dictate the way that words are structured and can be changed to alter the meaning, for example the correct way to use past tense or plurals.	We know we say 'Today I walk,' but we say 'Yesterday I walked.'
Narrative skills		
Non-verbal communication	Communication that does not include words or talking.	Facial expression/ body language

Term	Definition	For example
Phonology	The system of speech sounds and the way sounds are used and combined to produce speech.	Children with delayed phonology might make errors such as saying 'd' instead of 's', so say *'dun'* instead of *'sun'*.
Phonological disorder	Describes difficulties learning and organising all the speech sounds that are needed in order for children to have clear speech. A child with phonological disorder will have speech which sounds like that of a child much younger than them, or that sounds muddled. They might make errors that are unusual, and don't follow expected patterns.	Children with phonological disorder might be able to make all the right speech sounds, or can learn to do this relatively quickly, but don't always use them in the correct places in words and can take some time to learn this, e.g. using different speech sounds so 'horse' becomes 'port' and 'sheep' becomes 'peet'.

Term	Definition	For example
Pragmatics	The way we understand and use language/ communication skills in a social way, interacting with another person. Includes understanding non-verbal communication – e.g. facial expression, body posture.	Most children know that you would talk differently to your friends than to your teacher as they understand how to 'use' language the right way.
Pragmatic language impairment (PLI)	A difficulty understanding the social aspects of language, for example the way we use language with others appropriately, in a social way.	
Prosody	The term used to refer to elements that make our speech sound different such as loudness, how fast we talk, intonation and stress.	When we want to make something clear to others, we might stress the important words.
Receptive language	Understanding and comprehension of spoken and written language. A child with receptive language difficulties will find it hard to understand the words and sentences that others are saying to them.	

Term	Definition	For example
Semantics	Understanding the meanings of words and phrases.	
Semantic-pragmatic disorder	Describes the difficulties that children have with semantics and pragmatics, so problems with word meanings and how language is used. For example they find it hard to describe a story and keep to the topic without wandering off to talk about other things.	
SEN	Special Educational Needs	
SLCN	Speech, Language and Communication Needs	
SLI	Specific Language Impairment, or Specific Speech and Language Impairment.	
Social interaction	The ways that we interact with others in a social way, for example in conversations.	
Social skills	Skills important for interacting socially with others.	Eye contact Turn-taking

Term	Definition	For example
Syntax	The rules for assembling words into meaningful sentences (see also Grammar).	
Verbal Dyspraxia	Difficulty planning and sequencing sounds into words. There might be difficulties with making speech sounds and sequencing sounds and words appropriately, meaning that speech is very difficult to understand.	
Vocabulary	The collection of words that a child is able to understand and/or use.	
Word-finding difficulties	Difficulties recalling and using specific words, despite understanding them. Often characterised by repetitions, made up words and using unspecific vocabulary – e.g. 'That one'.	

Appendix 2

Questions YOU should ask the professionals

The following questions will
be helpful to find out the
ways a school would support
a child with SLI:

Q: What do teachers/TAs
know about SLI? Have they
had any training?

Some staff in specialist
settings will know about SLI
and should have had some
training. In a mainstream
school there may be staff that
have received some training
from the SLT, or during inset
training. It would be helpful
to ask if those working with
your child attended the
training, or if the school
would be willing to arrange
more training for them.

Q: How do you work with the
professionals that support
my child, e.g. a Speech
and Language Therapist/
Educational Psychologist?

A mainstream school might
say that when the SLT/EP
visits the school some of the
time is spent working with
your child. They should also
say that some time is spent
meeting with key people
such as the class teacher and
teaching assistant, sharing
information and supporting
the way your child is included
in the classroom.

An SLT should contribute to
an Individual Education Plan
(IEP) that may be written to
support your child and there
should be opportunities for
school staff to contact the
professionals for support
if needed. It might be that
the SLT goes into school to

offer training to the staff. In specialist provision such as a language resource or specialist school, the teaching staff should liaise closely with the SLT and teaching and therapy should be closely linked.

Q: How are parents and SLTs involved in target setting through the Individual Education Plan (IEP)?

This should happen if your child is at School Action, School Action Plus or has a statement, refer to SLI & SEN. An SLT should be invited to contribute to any IEP being set, and targets should be regularly reviewed. Parents should also be invited to discuss targets with the school and input to ideas and reviews. This should happen regardless of where your child goes to school.

Q: How do teachers communicate with parents regarding their child with SLI?

In many schools a home/ school communication book is used by teachers and TAs working with a child. This is an excellent idea as it allows parents and staff to communicate about anything important and share information. There should also be an opportunity for you to meet with the school regularly to share information.

Q: What happens in class to help children understand and work with others to communicate their messages?

You can expect to hear staff in a school talk about the communication-supportive features described earlier to enable a child to understand and communicate.

Specialist schools and language resources will have the features as part of their specialist practice; mainstream schools should be able to provide opportunities for communication and support for understanding with some simple adaptations.

Q: How are parents informed of current targets and ways they can support at home?

Parents should always be informed about any targets that are set for their child as part of the IEP. The school might also communicate some smaller, day to day targets via the home/school communication book. Parents can also expect SLTs to discuss their therapy targets with them, particularly when they have seen the child at school without the parent present.

SLTs and teachers should also give parents ideas about ways that they can help at home, either through suggested homework activities, or by giving strategies that the child and parent might find useful for supporting communication at home.

There are also some questions that you might find useful to ask your child's SLT:

Q: How do SLTs work in schools? How do their targets fit in with a child's school work?

An SLT should liaise closely with a school if they are a visiting professional; often language resources and specialist schools have SLTs who are regular staff members.

The SLT should make time to meet with school staff as well as see the child, and to share information from both sides.

The SLT working in school should have good knowledge of the National Curriculum and the Early Years Foundation Stage as they will then be able to link the work that they do with what is happening in school, and provide opportunities and adaptations that allow a child to access the teaching as much as possible. This should be the case regardless of the type of school a child goes to.

Q: How often will they visit the school?

This will vary according to the area that you live in, the type of difficulties that your child has, and the severity of their needs. You can expect the SLT to give you clear information about how often they plan to go to the school and to give you feedback after their visit.

Useful organisations

The following organisations will be able to provide you with helpful information and/or advice about SLI and SEN, including other types of SLCN, and how to support your child

Afasic
Afasic is the UK charity which helps children and young people with SLI, their families and the professionals working with them.
afasic.org.uk

I CAN
I CAN is the children's communication charity. We exist to ensure that children who struggle to communicate are not left out or left behind. Our vision is a world where all children and young people who struggle to communicate get the help they need so that they can have a happy childhood, make progress at school and thrive as adults.
ican.org.uk

The Communication Trust

The Communication Trust aims to raise awareness of the importance of speech, language and communication across the children's workforce and to enable practitioners to access the best training and expertise to support the communication needs of all children.
thecommunicationtrust.org.uk

Parent Partnership Services

Parent Partnership Services (PPS) are statutory services offering information, advice and support to parents and carers of children and young people with special educational needs (SEN).
parentpartnership.org.uk

Advisory Centre for Education (ACE)

ACE provide lots of information about all aspects of education, including statutory assessment.
ace-ed.org.uk

SOS!SEN

A website for parents seeking information about the world of special educational needs.
sossen.org.uk

IPSEA

IPSEA is a national charity providing free legally based advice to families who have children with special educational needs.
ipsea.org.uk

Appendix 4

Notes

What I want to tell someone about my child
(birth/early years/school experiences)...

What they are good at/What they find hard....